Santa Tita & Cocoa

To Believing

By

Isabel Kuri

Illustrated by

Nicorene Stassen

Hello! This book tells my story and allows you to color it how you imagine it.

www.caleleiproductions.com

CALELEI PRODUCTIONS

First Published in the United States of America by Calelei™ Productions LLC

IDENTIFIERS: LCCN: 2022921908

ISBN (Hardcover): 978-1-958807-30-9
ISBN (Paperback): 978-1-958807-31-6
ISBN (eBook English): 978-1-958807-32-3
ISBN (Coloring - English): 978-1-958807-34-7

This Book's ISBN: 978-1-958807-34-7

ISBN (Hardcover - Spanish): 978-1-958807-35-4
ISBN (Paperback - Spanish): 978-1-958807-36-1
ISBN (eBook Spanish): 978-1-958807-37-8
ISBN (Coloring - Spanish): 978-1-958807-39-2

CYAC: Christmas - Fiction I Reindeer

ABOUT THIS BOOK

"Santa Tita and Cocoa" By Isabel Kuri Illustrated By Nicorene Stassen

First Edition, December 2022 I First Print, December 2022 I English Language

The fonts used were "Christmas Bells" for the title, "Bellota" for the story, and "Encode Sans" for all other text. The illustrations in this book were created with Clip Studio Paint Ex by Nicorene Stassen. Please note that the publisher is not responsible for any other website other than the publishers', or its content. Visit us anytime at https://www.caleleiproductions.com

Follow our tree planting initiative at https://www.caleleiproductions.com/trees

It's one week to Christmas

there's a chill in the air,

The excitement of the season

can be felt everywhere.

It's one week to Christmas

and up in the North Pole,

Little Cocoa is ready

for the thrill of it all!

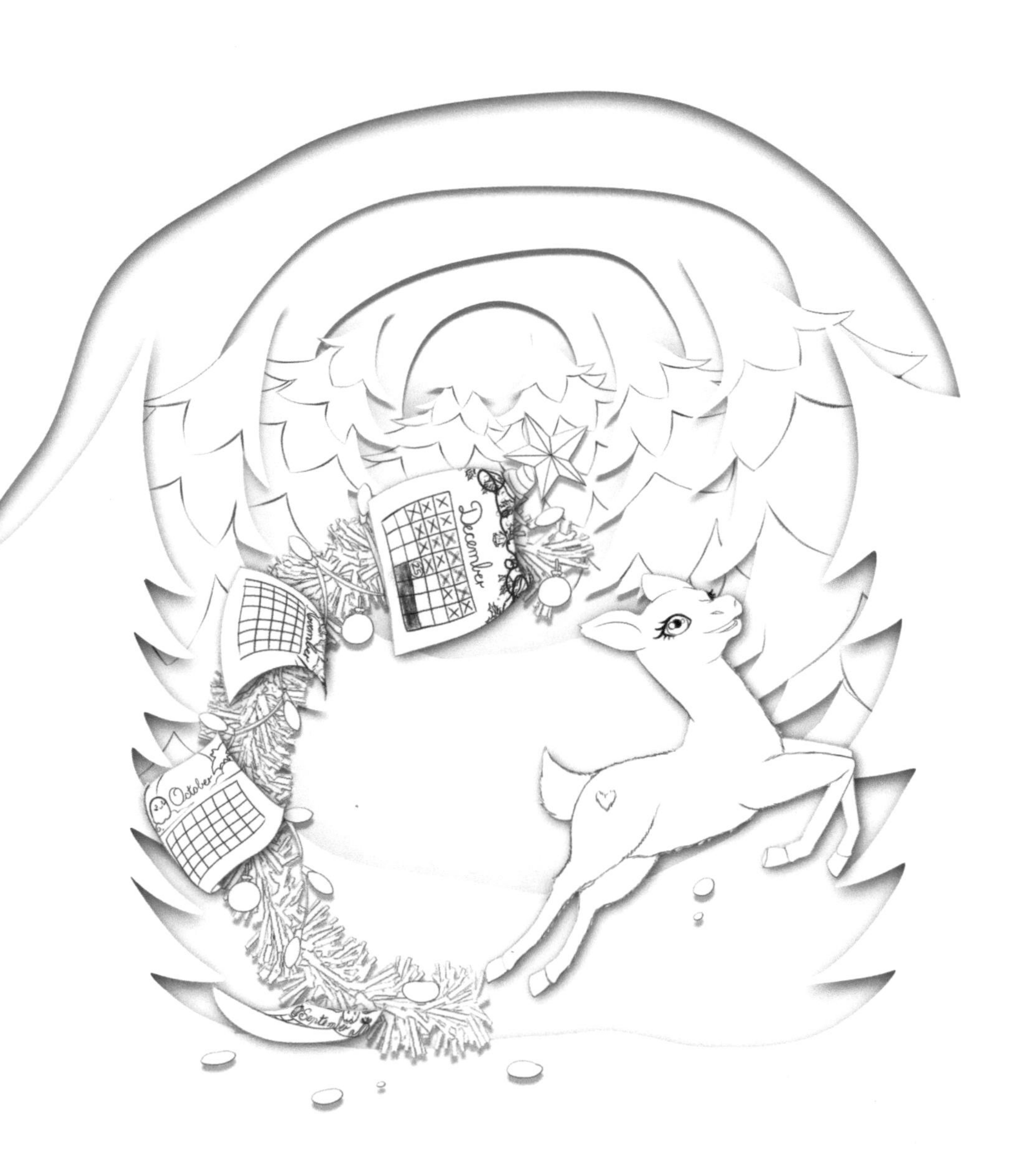

Reindeer training started

with the first snow of Spring,

When the bells of

Christmas planning

loudly began to ring.

s Santa Clause works diligently

with the elves at the shop,

Santa Tita is in the field

running rounds of "Reindeer Hop!"

She needs to be sure

the team is healthy

to fly well beyond the big night,

And so that on Christmas Eve

everything goes right!

Cocoa's biggest dream
is to join Santa's sleigh.
She prepares and she trains,
every day after day.

She's been paying attention
to what the big reindeer do,
to make sure she is ready
and can fly the sleigh too!

She's watched Comet

fly over the moving trapeze,

and Dancer and Prancer

use the trampolines.

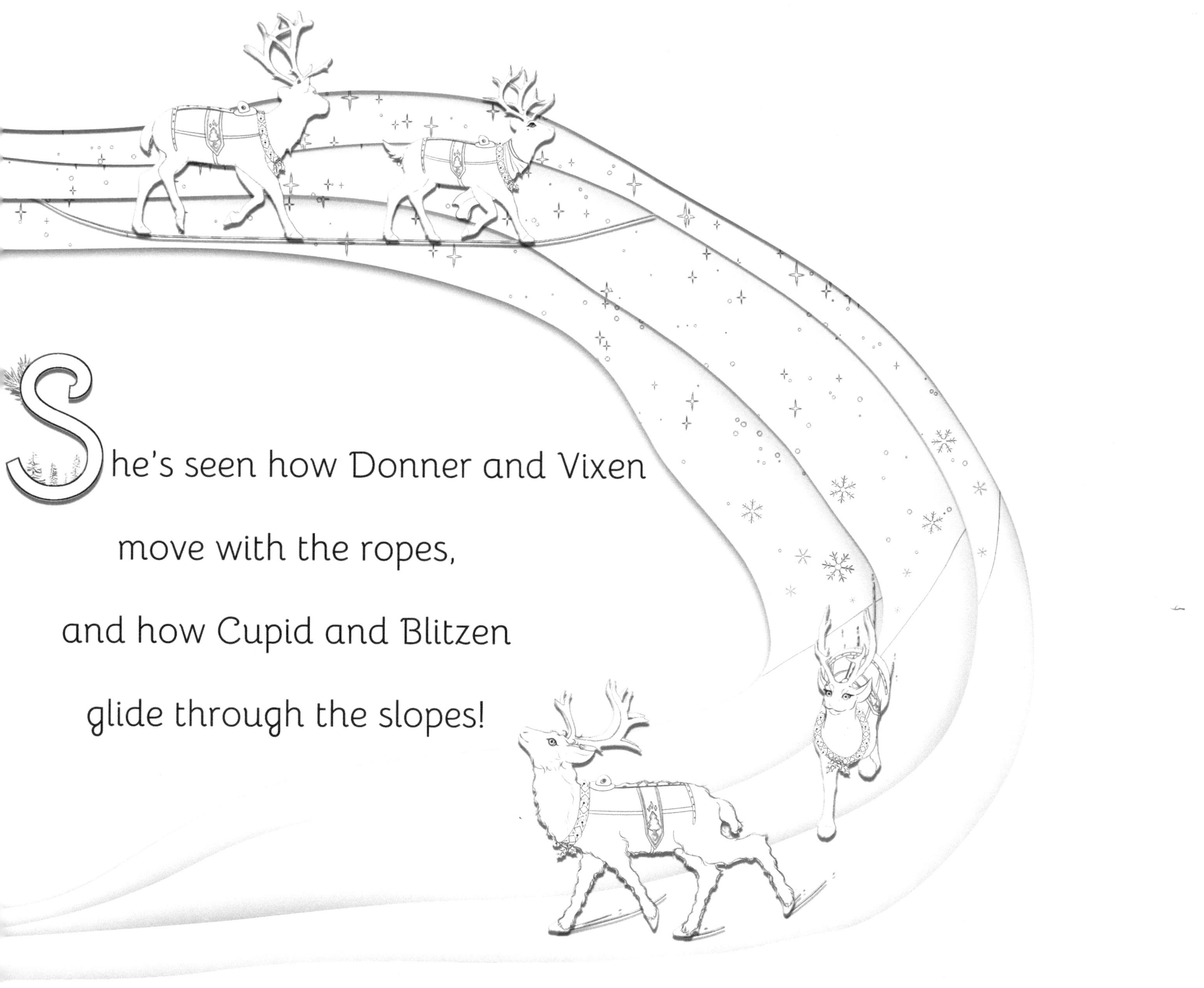

She's seen how Donner and Vixen

move with the ropes,

and how Cupid and Blitzen

glide through the slopes!

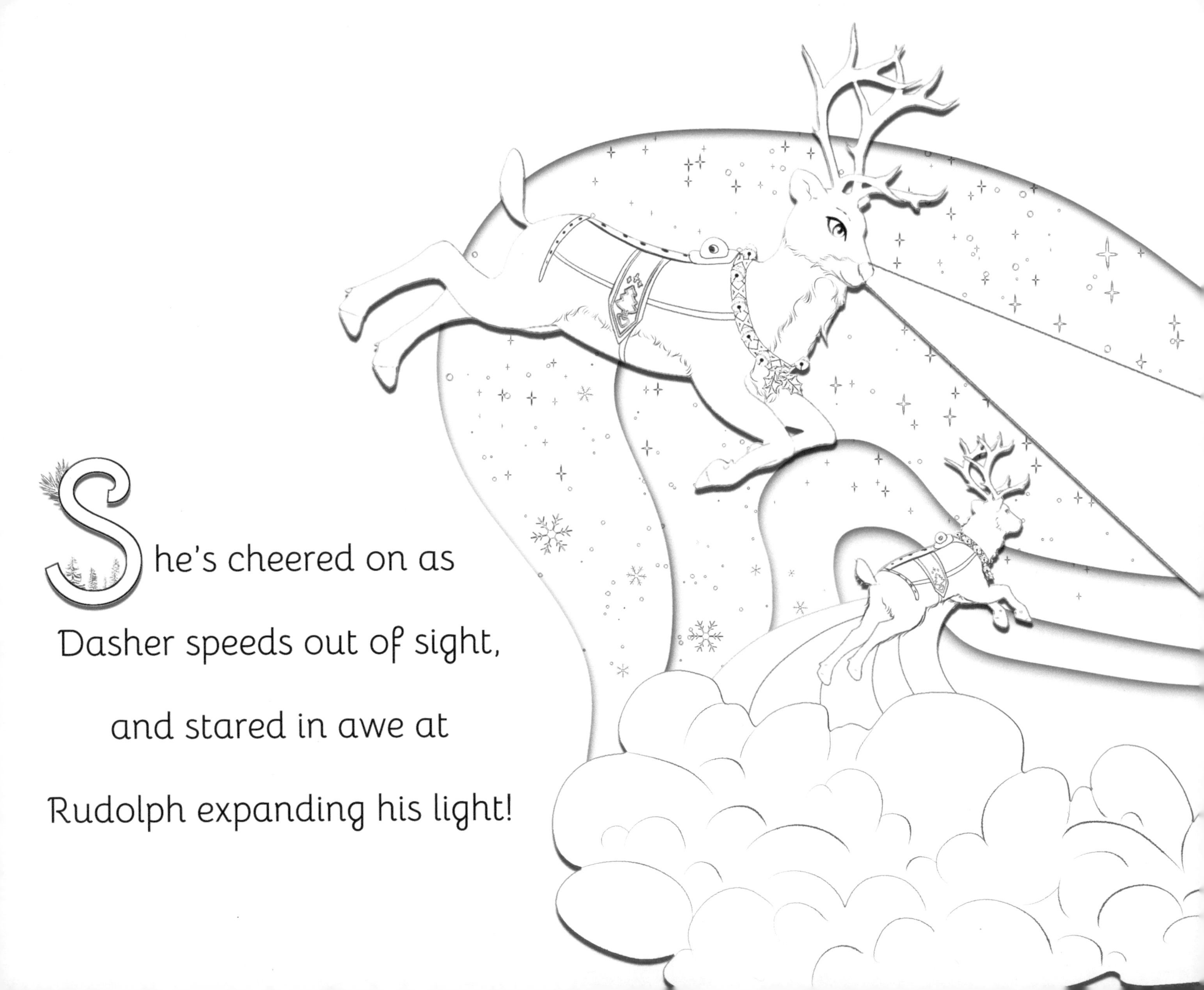

She's cheered on as

Dasher speeds out of sight,

and stared in awe at

Rudolph expanding his light!

She's memorized their movements,

their steps, and their posts,

She knows she can do it,

it's what she wants most!

Today the field is empty

as it's time to rest,

for tomorrow Santa Tita

will give them a big test.

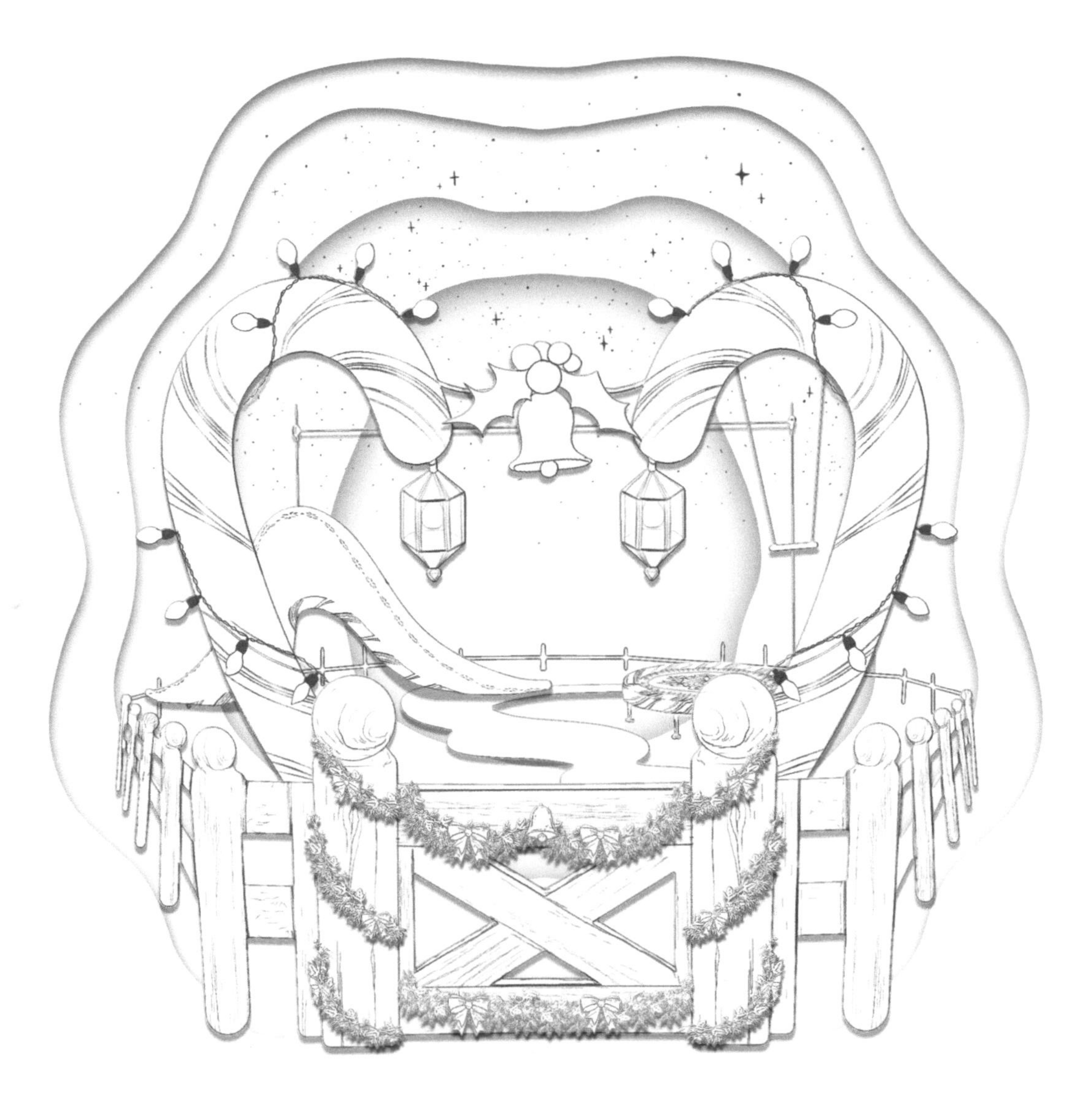

ocoa goes to the field and cheers herself on.

She knows what to do, this shouldn't take long.

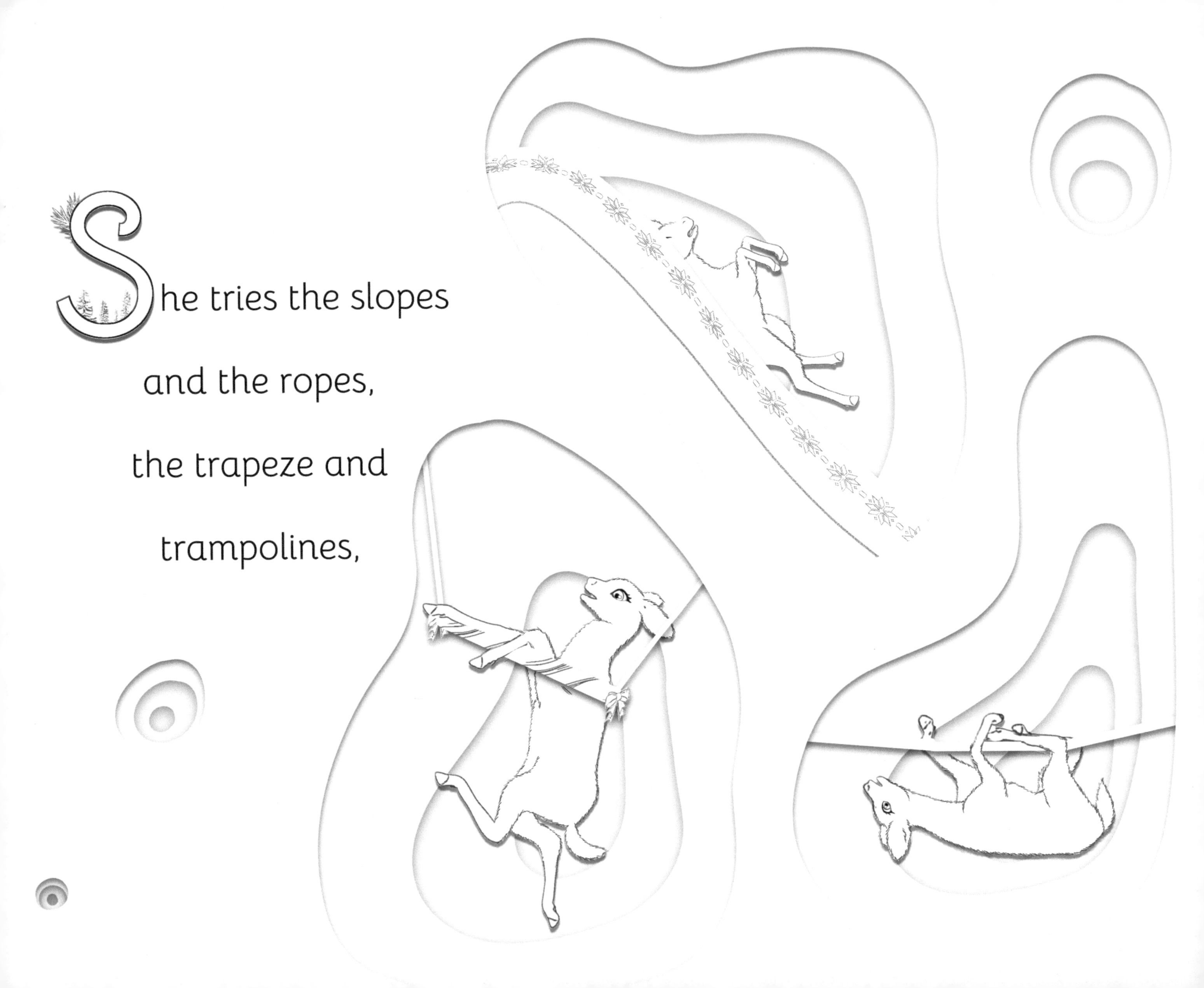

She tries the slopes
and the ropes,
the trapeze and
trampolines,

Yet "Reindeer Hop"

is not quite all that it

seems...

he sighs and stares down

at her little hooves,

She is doing all she can.

She's done the same moves!

Why is it she can't do it
just as they do?
Is she forgetting a step?
Or maybe even two?

As she thinks

and she ponders

Santa's reindeer appear:

"Hello dear Cocoa,

we saw you were near..."

Cocoa tries

to clear the tears

streaming from her eyes,

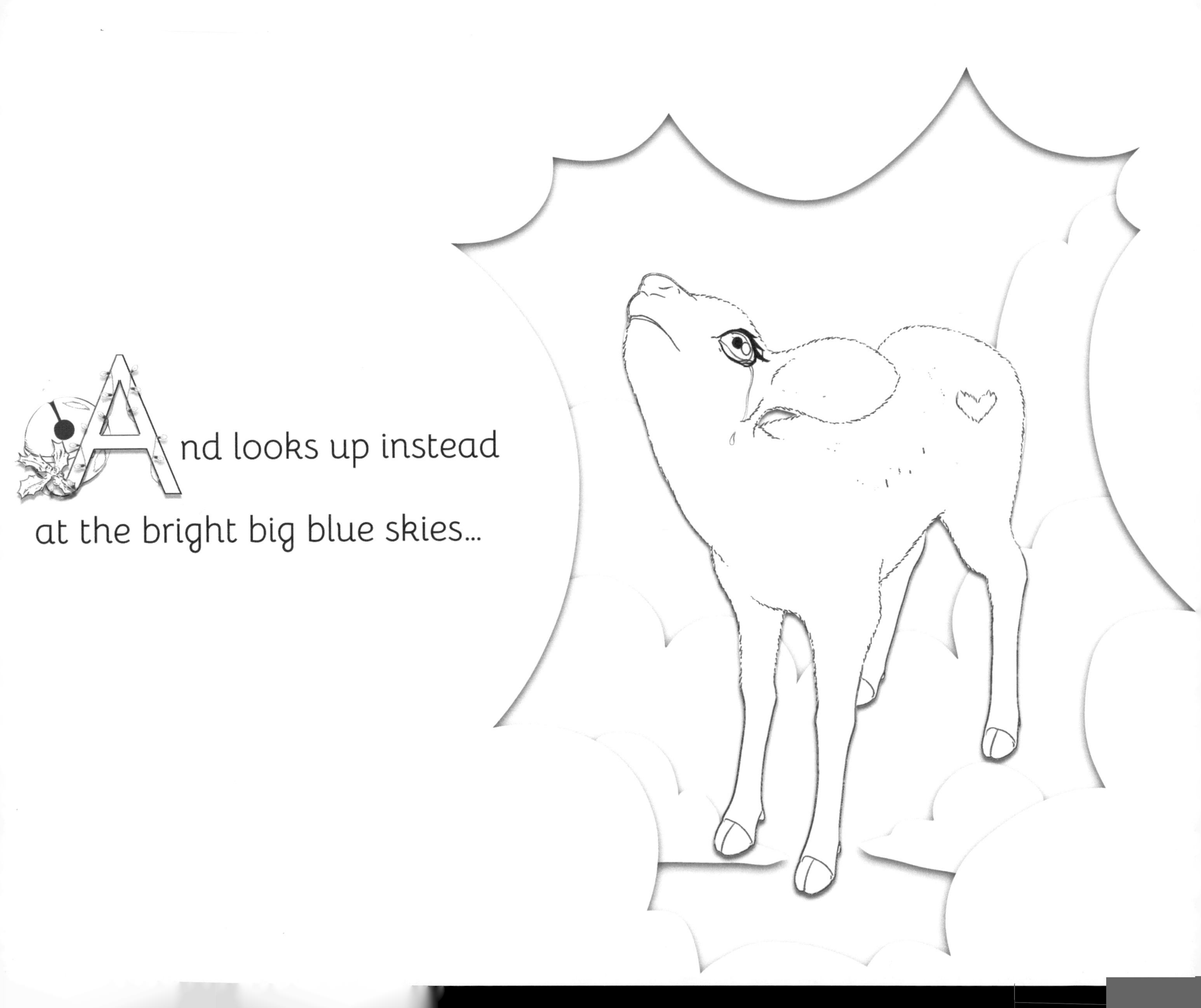

And looks up instead

at the bright big blue skies...

"I tried to do everything,

just everything you do,

and nothing was right,

yet I am a reindeer too!"

As they smile and remember

they tell Cocoa the truth:

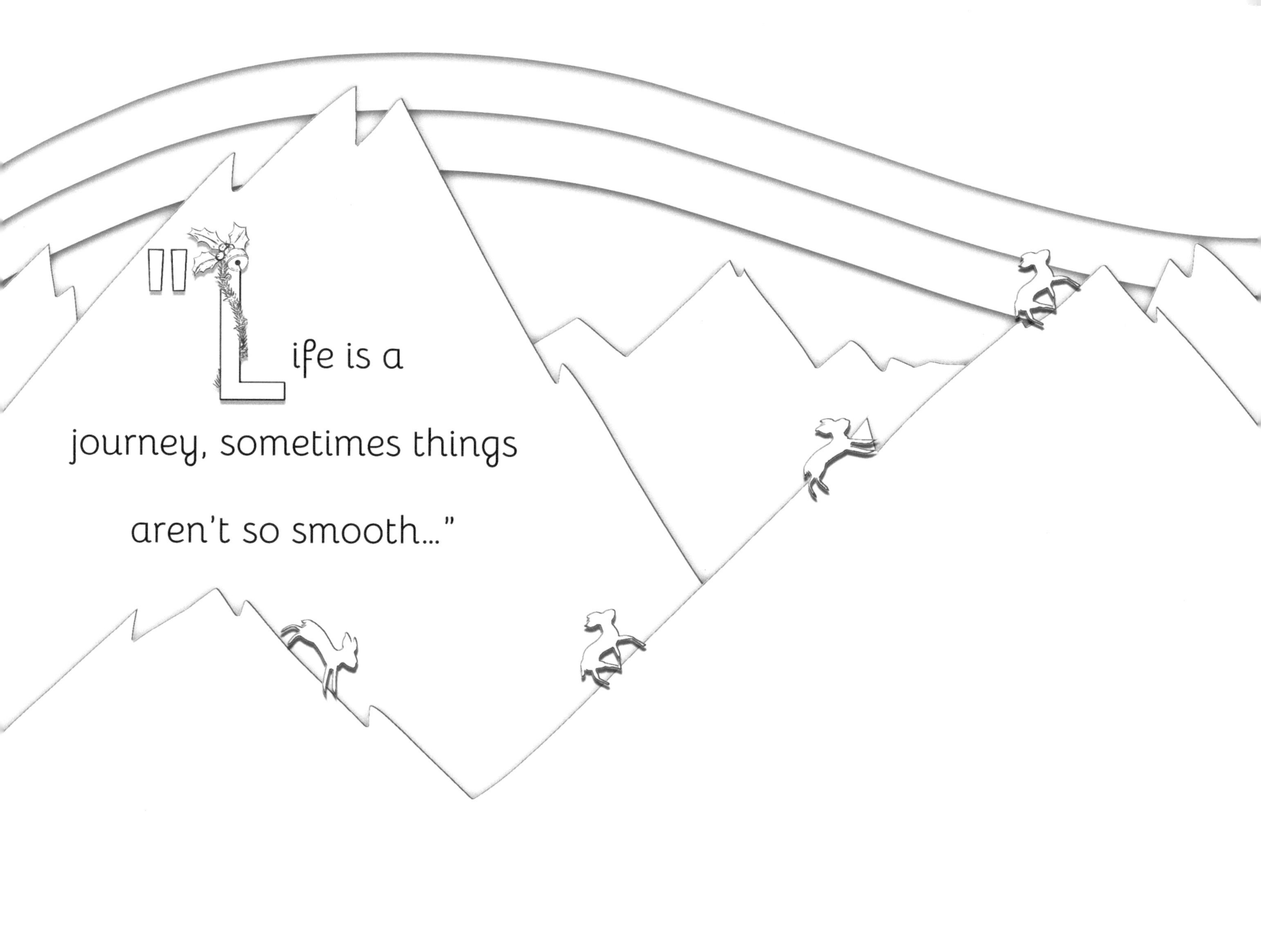

"Life is a journey, sometimes things aren't so smooth..."

"When I first started," says Comet,

"It wasn't a breeze.
Then Santa Tita thought
up the moving trapeze!"

"When I first started,"

says Blitzen with care,

"I couldn't keep my calm in,

not even for a dare.

Santa Tita noticed and

she built me the slope.

"Now I can speed through the night

and not tug on the rope."

"When I first started,"

says Rudolph

remembering the time,

"Well you know my story, no one quite liked my shine.

It was Santa Tita who told Santa Clause of my bright reddish feature, and you see now how it goes."

"It's part of the start"

Says Santa Tita joining in,

"Things are different for everyone,

we learn as we begin.

Sweet Cocoa

We know it can be daunting at first

it's ok, you'll find your own thing

and then you'll just rehearse.

If you know deep inside
it's what you want to do,
just follow your heart
and you'll find a way through."

"I could still do it?"

Cocoa stands up excited

"There is a way through?

Will I be able to do it just as you do?

Will you teach me how?

I am ready to start.

Should we start it now?

I'll do every part!

Will I be able to do

what I couldn't before?

How can I do it ?

Do I need to learn more?"

"Sometimes things change
as we learn and we grow,
you just have to stay open
to your heart's inner flow.

And if you keep steady
and find joy in each part,
by the time things get easy
you'll forget of the start.

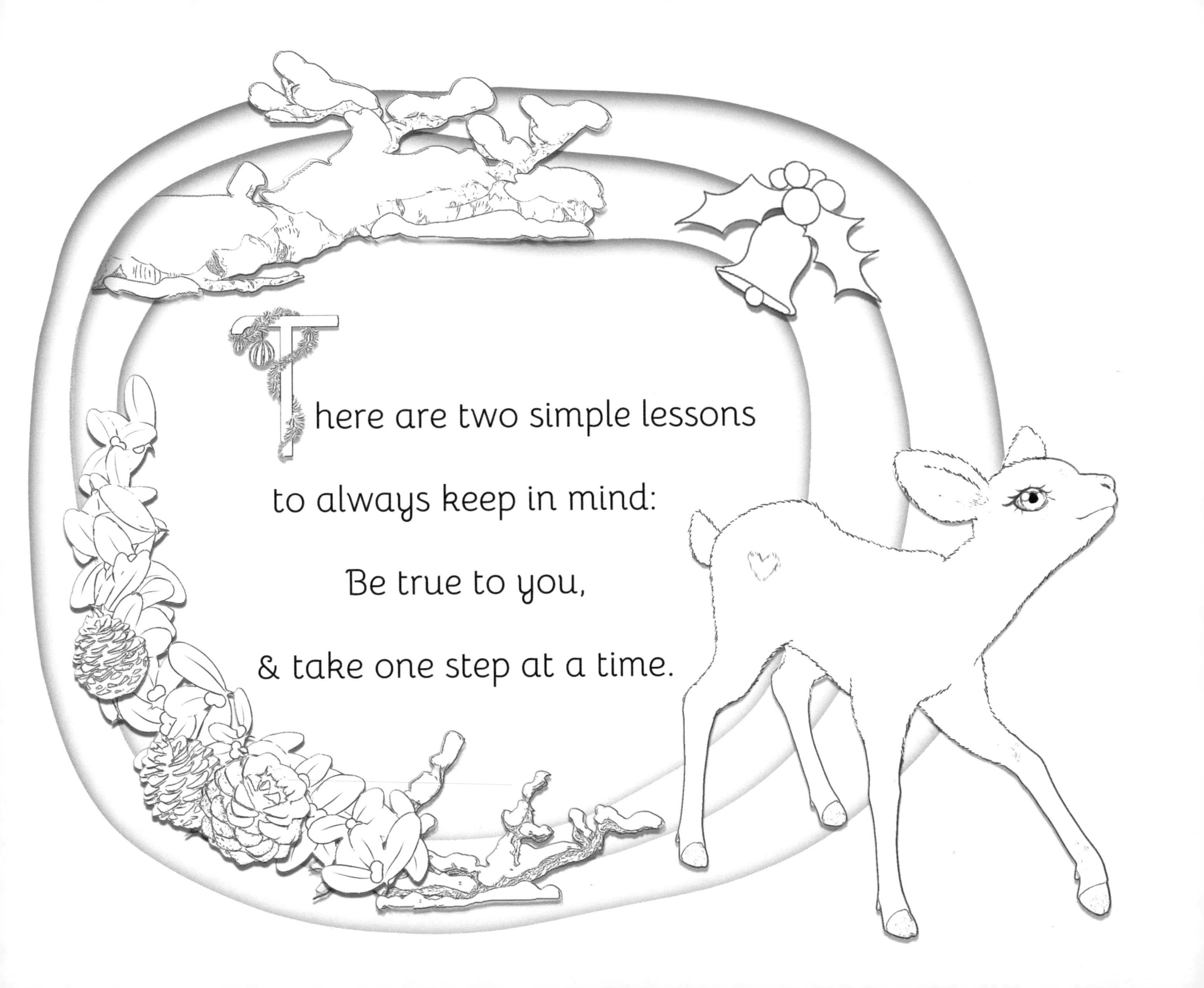

There are two simple lessons

to always keep in mind:

Be true to you,

& take one step at a time.

As you are learning
remember what makes you you.
For no one can do things
quite like you do!

Only you have the sound in your ears,

and the smells in your nose.

Only you know with your eyes

what you call far and close.

Only you know your strength,

and your courage within.

If you start from there

it's a guaranteed win!

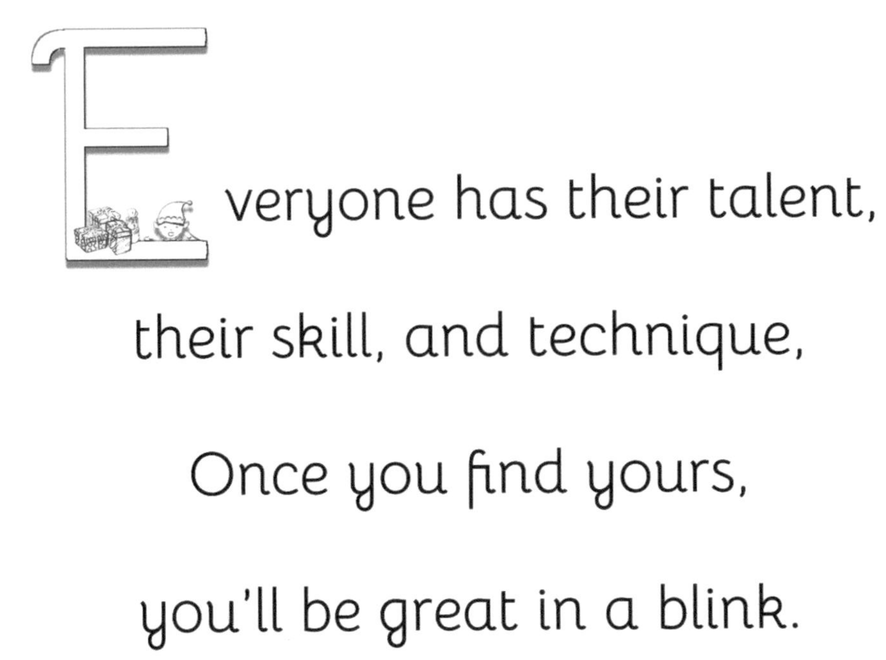

Everyone has their talent,

their skill, and technique,

Once you find yours,

you'll be great in a blink.

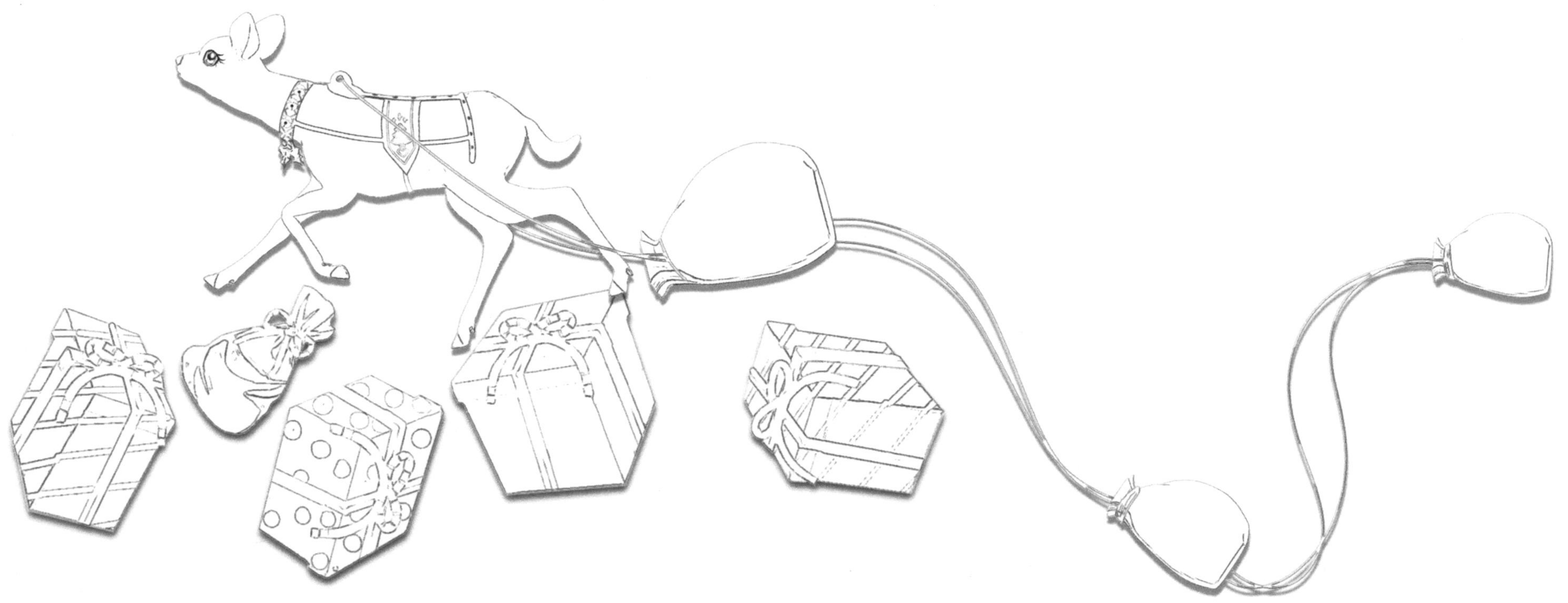

"I will be here with you
every step of the way
to make sure you are ready
for you own big day!"

As the reindeer get ready

for the long Christmas night

Santa Tita and Cocoa

test new ways for her flight.

Perhaps you'll see Cocoa
tonight or next year,
And you'll know that she did it
when you hear her loud cheer!

Cocoa's notes on success
"If there is something in your heart
that you want to do
Keep dreaming and remember,
that as you do you
You will always find a way
for your dreams to come true!"

Made With Love

Isabel Kuri

"I love to write. Writing is my favorite window into possibility. I write what I see from my window into the world."

What do you see from yours?

Author

Nicorene Stassen

"Magic and Fiction fascinate me. I enjoy bringing these stories to life, adding little specks of magic to our world one brushstroke at a time."

What would you like to add?

Illustrator

www.caleleiproductions.com

Printed in the USA
CPSIA information can be obtained
at www.ICGtesting.com
LVHW060716161223
766521LV00043B/568